Some singing, Lord

Hymns and songs for children
chosen by Beatrice Harrop

Words edition

A & C Black · London

Published by A. & C. Black (Publishers) Ltd. 35 Bedford Row London WC1R 4JH
© 1973 A. & C. Black Ltd.
Reprinted 1973, 1974 (three times), 1976 (three times), 1977, 1979, 1981, 1983
ISBN 0 7136 1847 7
Printed in Great Britain by Hollen Street Press Limited, Slough, Berkshire

Contents

Acknowledgements

For help in compiling this selection of hymns, the publishers are grateful to Pat Lloyd, Deputy Head of Great Staughton County Primary School, Huntingdon, and to Peggy Blakeley. They also thank Mary Collins, Head of Grange County Infant School, Gosport, Hampshire, Sarah Evans of Newton Hall Nursery, Durham City, and Ian Wragg, R.E. Adviser to Derbyshire Education Committee, for helpful advice and suggestions. Hymns 17, 18, 36, 38, 45, 54 and 59 have been specially written for this book by Peggy Blakeley. The cover design and illustrations are by C. R. Evans.

The following have kindly granted their permission for the reprinting of hymns and songs which are their copyright:

Sister Oswin and Geoffrey Chapman Publishers for "Who's that sitting in the sycamore tree" from *Let God's Children Sing* and "Hurray for Jesus" and "Now Jesus One Day" from *Sing Children of the Day*.

Crown Publishers Inc. for "O Lord! Shout for joy!" from *American Negro Songs and Spirituals* edited by John W. Work © 1940 John W. Work.

Durham Music Ltd. for "The ink is black, the page is white" by David Arkin © 1956, 1957 and 1971 Templeton Publishing Co. Inc.

Essex Music Ltd. for "God bless the grass" by Malvina Reynolds © 1964 Schroder Music Co. and "If I had a hammer" by Lee Hays © 1958 and 1959 Ludlow Music Inc.

Galliard Ltd. for "Lord, I love to stamp and shout" by Reginald Barrett-Ayres and "Think of a world without any flowers" by Doreen Newport from *New Songs for the Church*; "We have a king who rides a donkey" by Fred Kaan from *Pilgrim Praise*; and "I danced in the morning" and "When I needed a neighbour" by Sydney Carter.

Miss D. M. Gill for "Come, let us remember the joys of the town".

Granada Publishing Ltd. for "The golden cockerel" and "At half past three" by Margaret Rose from *The Morning Cockerel* published by Rupert Hart-Davis Educational Publications Ltd.

David Higham Associates Ltd. for "Morning has broken" by Eleanor Farjeon.

High-Fye Music Ltd. for "I have seen the golden sunshine" by Charlie Chester and Benny Litchfield, "Stand up, clap hands" by Roger Dyer, "The journey of life" by V. Collison and "He gave me eyes" by Alan Pinnock.

National Christian Education Council for "Hands to work and feet to run" by Hilda M. Dodd, "See how the snowflakes are falling" and "Little birds in winter time" by Frederick A. Jackson and "O Jesus we are well and strong" by E. F. B. MacAlister.

The National Society for "Who can see the great wind blow" and "Jesus' hands were kind hands" by Margaret Cropper, and "The farmer comes to scatter the seed" by C. Hardie from *Hymns and Songs for Children*.

Oxford University Press for "When a knight won his spurs" by Jan Struther (1901–1953) from *Enlarged Songs of Praise*; "To God who makes all lovely things" and "In the early morning" by J. M. C. Crum (1872–1958); and "I love God's tiny creatures" by G. W. Briggs (1875–1959) from *Songs of Praise for Boys and Girls*.

Miss A. M. Pullen for "I'm very glad of God" and "We praise you for the sun".

Religious Education Press, a member of the Pergamon Group of Companies for "I love the sun" by Gwen F. Smith and "All the flowers are waking" by Winifred Barnard from *The Nursery Song and Picture Book*.

The Seabury Press Inc. for "God who put the stars in space" by L. S. Reed from *Sing for Joy* © 1961 The Seabury Press Inc. Compiled and edited by Norman and Margaret Mealy.

Viking Press Inc. for "Who built the ark?" from *Rolling Along in Song* by J. Rosamond Johnson © 1937 The Viking Press Inc., renewed 1965 by Mrs Nora E. Johnson.

Josef Weinberger Ltd. for "This is a lovely world" by Jane Palmer from *Praise Our Lord*.

Every effort has been made to trace copyright owners but should any acknowledgement of rights have been omitted, this will be rectified in subsequent editions on notification being received by the Publishers.

1

1 Father, we thank you for the night,
   And for the pleasant morning light;
   For rest and food and loving care
   And all that makes the day so fair.

2 Help us to do the things we should,
   To be to others kind and good;
   In all we do at work or play
   To grow more loving every day.

2

The golden cockerel
Crows in the morning,
Wake up, children,
Welcome the day.
God's bright sun is
Riding the heavens,
Chasing sleepiness away.
Father,
Gladly we greet you,
Here come
Running to meet you.
Please be
In us and near us,
Hallowing our work and play.

3

1   Morning has broken
Like the first morning,
Blackbird has spoken
Like the first bird.
Praise for the singing!
Praise for the morning!
Praise for them, springing
Fresh from the Lord!

2   Mine is the sunlight!
Mine is the morning
Here in the bright light
Of this fair day!
Praise with elation,
Praise every morning
God's re-creation
Of the new day!

4

O Lord! Shout for joy!
O Lord! Shout for joy!

1 Early in the morning,
Shout for joy!
Early in the morning,
Shout for joy!

2 Feel like shouting,
Shout for joy!
Feel like shouting,
Shout for joy!

3 Feel like praying,
Shout for joy!
Feel like praying,
Shout for joy!

4 Now I'm getting happy,
Shout for joy!
Now I'm getting happy,
Shout for joy!

5

1 Lord, I love to stamp and shout
  testing lungs and muscles out;
  other times I curl up still
  dreaming till I've had my fill.

2 Lord, I love to watch things fly,
  whizzing, zooming, flashing by;
  engines, aircraft, speedboats, cars,
  spacecraft shooting to the stars.

3 Lord, I love to probe and pry
  seeking out the reason why;
  looking inside things and out,
  finding what they're all about.

4 Lord, I'm many things and one
  though my life's not long begun;
  you alone my secret see
  what I am cut out to be.

6

1   I have seen the golden sunshine,
    I have watched the flowers grow,
    I have listened to the song birds
    And there's one thing now I know,
    They were all put there for us to share
    By someone so divine,
    And if you're a friend of Jesus,
        CLAP CLAP CLAP CLAP
    You're a friend of mine.

            I've seen the light, I've seen the light,
            And that's why my heart sings.
            I've known the joy, I've known the joy
            That loving Jesus brings.

2   I have seen the morning sunshine,
    I have heard the oceans roar,
    I have seen the flowers of springtime,
    And there's one thing I am sure,
    They were all put there for us to share
    By someone so divine,
    And if you're a friend of Jesus,
        CLAP CLAP CLAP CLAP
    You're a friend of mine.

7

1   Come, let us remember
        the joys of the town:
    Gay vans and bright buses
        that roar up and down,
    Shop windows and playgrounds
        and swings in the park,
    And street lamps that twinkle
        in rows after dark.

2   And let us remember
        the life in the street:
    The horses that pass us,
        the dogs that we meet;
    Grey pigeons, brown sparrows,
        and gulls from the sea,
    And folk who are friendly
        to you and to me.

3   We thank you, O God,
        for the numberless things
    And friends and adventures
        which every day brings.
    O may we not rest until
        all that we see
    In towns and in cities
        is pleasing to you.

8

1   This is a lovely world.
Birds in the trees above
Sing of a world that's made
By a God of love.

2   This is a joyful world
Where every girl and boy
Sings of a world that's made
By a God of joy.

9

1   To God who makes all lovely things
How happy must our praises be!
Each day a new surprise he brings
To make us glad his world to see.

2   How plentiful must be the mines
From which he gives his gold away;
In March he gives us celandines,
He gives us buttercups in May.

3   On winter nights his quiet flakes
Come falling, falling all the night,
And when the world next morning wakes
It finds itself all shining white.

4   He makes the sea that shines afar
With waves that dance unceasingly;
And every single little star
That twinkles in the evening sky.

5   He made the people that I meet,
The many people, great and small,
In home and school, and down the street,
And he made me to love them all.

10

Over the earth is a mat of green,
Over the green is dew,
Over the dew are the arching trees,
Over the trees the blue.
Across the blue are scudding clouds,
Over the clouds, the sun,
Over it all is the love of God,
Blessing us every one,
Blessing us every one.

11

The sun that shines across the sea,
The wind that whispers in the tree,
The lark that carols in the sky,
The fleecy clouds a-sailing by—
O, I am rich as rich can be,
For all these things belong to me!
O, I am rich as rich can be,
For all these things are mine,
For all these things are mine!

12

1   I love the sun,
       It shines on me,
       God made the sun,
       And God made me.

2   I love the stars,
       They twinkle on me,
       God made the stars,
       And God made me.

3   I love the rain,
       It splashes on me,
       God made the rain,
       And God made me.

4   I love the wind,
       It blows round me,
       God made the wind,
       And God made me.

5   I love the birds,
       They sing to me,
       God made the birds,
       And God made me.

13

1   We praise you for the sun,
The golden, shining sun,
That gives us healing, strength and joy,
We praise you for the sun.

2   We praise you for the rain,
The softly falling rain,
That gives us healing, strength and joy,
We praise you for the rain.

3   We praise you for your love,
Our friend and Father God,
Who gives us healing, strength and joy,
We praise you for your love.

14

Stand up, clap hands, shout thank you, Lord,
Thank you for the world I'm in.
Stand up, clap hands, shout thank you, Lord,
For happiness and peace within.

1   I look around and the sun's in the sky,
    I look around and then I think oh my!
    The world is such a wonderful place,
    And all because of the Good Lord's grace:

2   I look around and the creatures I see,
    I look around and it amazes me
    That every fox and bird and hare
    Must fit in a special place somewhere:

3   I look around at all the joy I've had,
    I look around and then it makes me glad
    That I can offer thanks and praise
    To him who guides me through my days:

15

1   Think of a world without any flowers,
Think of a world without any trees,
Think of a sky without any sunshine,
Think of the air without any breeze.
We thank you, Lord,
    for flowers and trees and sunshine,
We thank you, Lord,
    and praise your holy name.

2   Think of the world without any animals,
Think of a field without any herd,
Think of a stream without any fishes,
Think of a dawn without any bird.
We thank you, Lord,
    for all your living creatures,
We thank you, Lord,
    and praise your holy name.

3   Think of a world without any people,
Think of a street with no-one living there,
Think of a town without any houses,
No-one to love and nobody to care.
We thank you, Lord,
    for families and friendships,
We thank you, Lord,
    and praise your holy name.

16

1   For all the strength we have,
To run and leap and play,
For all our limbs so sound and strong,
We thank you, Lord, today.

2   Make all your children, Lord,
Healthy and strong like me,
To run and leap and shout and play,
And praise you in our glee.

17

1   Milk bottle tops and paper bags,
    Iron bedsteads, dirty old rags,
    Litter on the pavement,
    Paper in the park,
    Is this what we
        CLAP CLAP CLAP CLAP
    Really want to see?
        CLAP CLAP CLAP-CLAP CLAP
    No! No! No!

2   Old plastic bottles, silver foil,
    Chocolate wrapping, engine oil,
    Rubbish in the gutter,
    Junk upon the beach,
    Is this what we
        CLAP CLAP CLAP CLAP
    Really want to see?
        CLAP CLAP CLAP-CLAP CLAP
    No! No! No!

3   Help us, Lord, to find each day
    Ways to help to keep away
    That litter off the pavement,
    That rubbish off the beach.
    For this is what we
        CLAP CLAP CLAP CLAP
    Really want to see.
        CLAP CLAP CLAP-CLAP CLAP
    Yes! Yes! Yes!

18

1   Give to us eyes
That we may truly see,
Flight of a bird,
The shapes in a tree,
Curve of a hillside,
Colours in a stone,
Give to us seeing eyes, O Lord.

2   Give to us ears
That we may truly hear,
Music in birdsong,
Rippling water clear,
Whine of the winter wind,
Laughter of a friend,
Give to us hearing ears, O Lord.

3   Give to us hands
That we may truly know,
Patterns in tree bark,
Crispness of the snow,
Smooth feel of velvet,
Shapes in a shell,
Give to us knowing hands, O Lord.

19

1   He gave me eyes so I could see
The wonders of the world.
Without my eyes I could not see
The other boys and girls.
He gave me ears so I could hear
The wind and rain and sea.
I've got to tell it to the world,
He made me.

2   He gave me lips so I could speak
And say what's in my mind.
Without my lips I could not speak
A single word or line.
He made my mind so I could think,
And choose what I should be.
I've got to tell it to the world,
He made me.

3   He gave me hands so I could touch,
And hold a thousand things.
I need my hands to help me write,
To help me fetch and bring.
These feet he made so I could run,
He meant me to be free.
I've got to tell it to the world,
He made me.

20

1   Praise to God for things we see,
The growing flower, the waving tree,
Our mother's face, the bright blue sky
Where birds and clouds go floating by,
Praise to God for seeing.

2   Praise to God for things we hear,
The voices of our playmates dear,
The merry bells, the song of birds,
Stories and tunes and kindly words,
Praise to God for hearing.

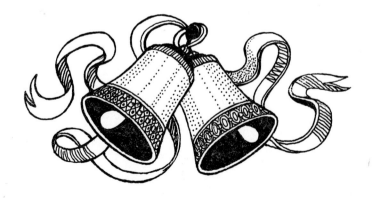

21

1   Hands to work and feet to run –
God's good gifts to me and you;
Hands and feet he gave to us
To help each other the whole day through.

2   Eyes to see and ears to hear –
God's good gifts to me and you;
Eyes and ears he gave to us
To help each other the whole day through.

3   Minds to think and hearts to love –
God's good gifts to me and you;
Minds and hearts he gave to us
To help each other the whole day through.

22

1   I'm very glad of God:
His love takes care of me,
In every lovely thing I see
God smiles at me!

2   I'm very glad of God:
His love takes care of me,
In every lovely sound I hear
God speaks to me!

23

1 Kum ba yah, my Lord, kum ba yah,
   Kum ba yah, my Lord, kum ba yah,
   Kum ba yah, my Lord, kum ba yah,
     O Lord, kum ba yah.

2 Someone's singing, Lord, kum ba yah

3 Someone's praying, Lord, kum ba yah

4 Someone's hungry, Lord, kum ba yah

5 Someone's suffering, Lord, kum ba yah

6 Someone's lonely, Lord, kum ba yah

24

1   A little tiny bird,
With sweet and cheerful song,
God watches, thinks and cares for
All the day long.

2   A little helpless babe,
That knows not right from wrong,
God wakes a mother's love for
All the day long.

3   A little trustful child,
Singing to God his song,
God loves to hear the music
All the day long.

25

1   Can you count the stars that brightly
Twinkle in the midnight sky?
Can you count the clouds, so lightly
O'er the meadows floating by?
God, the Lord, doth mark their number
With his eyes that never slumber;
He hath made them,
He hath made them,
He hath made them, every one.

2   Do you know how many children
Rise each morning bright and gay?
Can you count their jolly voices,
Singing sweetly day by day?
God hears all the happy voices,
In their merry songs rejoices;
And he loves them,
And he loves them,
And he loves them, every one.

26

1   When lamps are lighted in the town,
    The boats sail out to sea;
    The fishers watch when night comes down,
    They work for you and me.

2   When little children go to rest,
    Before they sleep, they pray
    That God will bless the fishermen
    And bring them back at day.

3   The boats come in at early dawn,
    When children wake in bed;
    Upon the beach the boats are drawn,
    And all the nets are spread.

4   God has watched o'er the fishermen
    Far on the deep dark sea,
    And brought them safely home again,
    Where they are glad to be.

27

1 God bless the grass
    that grows through the crack,
They roll the concrete over it
    to try and keep it back.
The concrete gets tired
    of what it has to do,
It breaks and it buckles
    and the grass grows through;
And God bless the grass.

2 God bless the truth
    that fights towards the sun,
They roll the lies over it
    and hope that it is done.
It moves through the ground
    and reaches for the air,
And after a while
    it is growing everywhere;
And God bless the truth.

28

1   The journey of life
May be easy, may be hard,
There'll be danger on the way;
With Christ at my side
I'll do battle as I ride
'Gainst the foe that would lead me astray:

>Will you ride, ride, ride
>With the King of Kings,
>Will you follow my leader true;
>Will you shout Hosanna
>To the lowly Son of God,
>Who died for me and you?

2   My burden is light
And a song is in my heart
As I travel on life's way;
For Christ is my Lord
And he's given me his word
That by my side he'll stay:

29

1   I danced in the morning
When the world was begun,
And I danced in the moon
And the stars and the sun,
And I came down from heaven
And I danced on the earth –
At Bethlehem I had my birth.

> Dance, then, wherever you may be,
> I am the Lord of the Dance, said he,
> And I'll lead you all, wherever you may be,
> And I'll lead you all in the dance, said he.

2   I danced for the scribe
And the pharisee,
But they would not dance
And they wouldn't follow me.
I danced for the fishermen,
For James and John –
They came with me
And the dance went on.

30

1   Now Jesus one day
Went down to the shore,
And hundreds of people
Who'd heard him before
Followed him to listen,
Followed him to listen,
And the waves all went splash,
   splash, splash, splash.

2   He got in a boat
And put out to sea
Where people could see him
As plain as could be.
They settled down to listen,
Settled down to listen,
And the waves all went splash,
   splash, splash, splash.

3   Then he sent them home
To village and town,
And he said to Peter:
"Now, let your net down."
Peter started fishing,
Peter started fishing,
And the waves all went splash,
   splash, splash, splash.

4   The fishes swarmed in;
The net nearly broke.
Then Jesus said to him:
"Come fishing for folk.
Come and follow me,
Come and follow me,"
And the waves all went splash,
    splash, splash, splash,
    splash!

31

1   It fell upon a summer day,
When Jesus walked in Galilee,
The mothers from a village brought
Their children to his knee.

2   He took them in his arms, and laid
His hands on each remembered head;
"Suffer these little ones to come
To me," he gently said.

32

1   Who's that sitting in the sycamore tree?
It's Zacchaeus who's as mean as can be.
Down on the ground, he's so short he cannot see
Over the crowd to Jesus.

        Come down, Zacchaeus, down from the tree.
        Come down, Zacchaeus, give the Lord his tea.

2   Who's that coming down the Jericho street?
Hot and hungry on his two tired feet?
He's the one whom the crowd has come to greet,
Raising three cheers for Jesus.

3   Who'll take Jesus home for tea and a rest?
Each one there would welcome him as a guest.
Surely he'll pick out the holiest and the best:
But up in the tree looks Jesus.

4   Who's that knocking at the poor folk's door?
Sharing his money as he's never done before?
It's Zacchaeus who's not mean any more;
All for the love of Jesus.

33

1   Jesus' hands were kind hands,
    Doing good to all;
    Healing pain and sickness,
    Blessing children small;
    Washing tired feet
    And saving those who fall;
    Jesus' hands were kind hands,
    Doing good to all.

2   Take my hands, Lord Jesus,
    Let them work for you,
    Make them strong and gentle,
    Kind in all I do;
    Let me watch you, Jesus,
    Till I'm gentle too,
    Till my hands are kind hands,
    Quick to work for you.

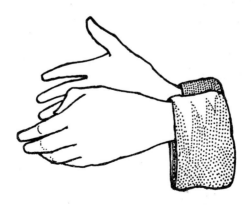

34

1 When a knight won his spurs,
In the stories of old,
He was gentle and brave,
He was gallant and bold;
With a shield on his arm
And a lance in his hand,
For God and for valour
He rode through the land.

2 No charger have I
And no sword by my side,
Yet still to adventure
And battle I ride,
Though back into storyland
Giants have fled,
And the knights are no more
And the dragons are dead.

3 Let faith be my shield
And let joy be my steed,
'Gainst the dragons of anger,
The ogres of greed;
And let me set free,
With the sword of my youth,
From the castle of darkness
The power of the truth.

35

1 When I needed a neighbour,
  Were you there, were you there?
When I needed a neighbour,
  Were you there?

  And the creed and the colour
   and the name won't matter,
  Were you there?

2 I was hungry and thirsty

3 I was cold, I was naked

4 When I needed a shelter

5 Wherever you travel,
  I'll be there, I'll be there,
Wherever you travel,
  I'll be there.

  And the creed and the colour
   and the name won't matter,
  I'll be there.

36

1   Look out for loneliness
If it should come your way,
Look out for loneliness,
Watch for it every day.
Look at home, look in school,
When you're walking in the street,
In the park and at the bus stop,
In the faces that you meet.
      Look out, look out, look out
      For loneliness.

2   Look out for strangers
Every once in a while,
Look out for strangers
Who need a friendly smile.
Give some love,
Give some warmth,
Give a hand in welcome too;
Bear in mind that one day soon
That stranger may quite well be you.
      Look out, look out, look out
      For loneliness.

37

1   If I had a hammer,
I'd hammer in the morning,
I'd hammer in the evening
All over this land.
I'd hammer out danger,
I'd hammer out a warning,
I'd hammer out love between
My brothers and my sisters,
All over this land.

2   If I had a bell,
I'd ring it in the morning,
I'd ring it in the evening
All over this land.
I'd ring out danger,
I'd ring out a warning,
I'd ring out love between
My brothers and my sisters,
All over this land.

3   If I had a song,
I'd sing it in the morning,
I'd sing it in the evening
All over this land.
I'd sing out danger,
I'd sing out a warning,
I'd sing out love between
My brothers and my sisters,
All over this land.

38

1   Think, think on these things:
Being a friend,
Giving a smile,
Or helping to make
Someone else's day worthwhile;
Think, think on these things.

2   Think, think on these things:
Unhappy and lost,
Friendless or old,
Or what it is like
To be hungry, to be cold;
Think, think on these things.

3   Think, think on these things:
Forgiving an ill,
Lending a hand,
Or trying to make
Other people understand;
Think, think on these things.

39

1   The ink is black, the page is white,
Together we learn to read and write,
To read and write.
And now a child can understand,
This is the law of all the land,
All the land!
The ink is black, the page is white,
Together we learn to read and write,
To read and write.

2   The board is black, the chalk is white,
The words stand out so clear and bright,
So clear and bright.
And now at last we plainly see
The alphabet of liberty,
Liberty!
The board is black, the chalk is white,
The words stand out so clear and bright,
So clear and bright.

3   A child is black, a child is white,
The whole world looks upon the sight,
A beautiful sight.
For very well the whole world knows,
This is the way that freedom grows,
Freedom grows!
A child is black, a child is white,
The whole world looks upon the sight,
A beautiful sight.

40

1   O Jesus, we are well and strong,
    And we can run about and play;
    But there are children who are sick,
    And have to be in bed all day.

2   We thank you for our health and strength;
    And, loving Lord, we pray you, bless
    The children who are weak and ill
    And suffer pain and weariness.

3   Lord, give us thoughtful, loving hearts;
    Show us kind deeds which we may do
    To help some sad or suffering one
    Till they are well and happy too.

41

1   All things which live below the sky,
Or move within the sea,
Are creatures of the Lord most high,
And brothers unto me.

2   I love to hear the robin sing,
Perched on the highest bough;
To see the rook with purple wing
Follow the shining plough.

3   I love to watch the swallow skim
The river in his flight;
To mark, when day is growing dim,
The glow worm's silvery light.

4   Almighty Father, King of kings,
The lover of the meek,
Make me a friend of helpless things,
Defender of the weak.

42

1   I love God's tiny creatures
That wander wild and free,
The coral-coated ladybird,
The velvet humming-bee;
Shy little flowers in hedge and dyke
That hide themselves away:
God paints them, though they are so small,
God makes them bright and gay.

2   Dear Father, who has all things made,
And cares about them all,
There's none too great for your great love,
Nor anything too small:
If you can spend such tender care
On things that grow so wild,
How wonderful your love must be
For me, your loving child.

43

1   Little birds in winter time
       Hungry are and poor;
       Feed them, for the Father's sake,
       Till the winter's o'er.

2   Throw them crumbs that you can spare
       Round about your door;
       Feed them, for the Father's sake,
       Till the winter's o'er.

44

Who built the ark?
Noah, Noah,
Who built the ark?
Brother Noah built the ark.

1   Now in come the animals two by two,
     Hippopotamus and kangaroo.

2   Now in come the animals four by four,
     Two through the window and two
          through the door.

3   Now in come the animals six by six,
     Elephant laughed at the monkey's tricks.

4   Now in come the animals eight by eight,
     Some were on time and the others were late.

5   Now in come the animals ten by ten,
     Five black roosters and five black hens.

6   Now Noah says, go shut that door,
     The rain's started dropping
          and we can't take more.

45

1   5, 4, 3, 2, 1 and zero,
Signals blast off into space,
Men in a rocket ride the sky,
Boom, boom, boom
On a journey to the moon.

2   Crackle, squeak through the atmosphere-o
Voices echo down to earth,
Men in a module come to rest,
Boom, boom, boom
On the highlands of the moon.

3   When they scan the universe-o
They must see our tiny world,
Part of a pattern made by God,
Boom, boom, boom
From the cold light of the moon.

4   Floating on a parachute-o
Through to splash-down, back to earth,
Thank you God, for this world you gave us,
(Either) Boom, boom, boom,
So unlike the cold old moon.

(Or)   Quite unlike the stark old moon,
Quite unlike the cold old moon,
Quite unlike that old unfriendly moon,
Boom, boom.

46

1   Twinkle, twinkle, little star,
How I wonder what you are,
Up above the world so high,
Like a diamond in the sky.

     Twinkle, twinkle, little star,
     How I wonder what you are.

2   When the blazing sun is gone,
When he nothing shines upon,
Then you show your little light,
Twinkle, twinkle all the night.

3   Then the traveller in the dark
Thanks you for your tiny spark;
Could he see which way to go
If you did not twinkle so?

47

1 God who put the stars in space,
  Who made the world we share,
  In his making made a place
  For me, and put me here.

2 Thank you, God, for stars in space
  And for the world we share.
  Thank you for my special place
  To love and serve you here.

48

1   All the flowers are waking,
     Spring has come again;
     God has sent the sunshine,
     God has sent the rain.

2   All the trees are waking,
     Spring has come again;
     God has sent the sunshine,
     God has sent the rain.

3   All the birds are singing,
     Spring has come again;
     Singing in the sunshine,
     Singing in the rain.

A verse for Winter

4   All the flowers are sleeping
     Underneath the ground;
     Sleeping in the winter,
     Sleeping safe and sound.

49

1   In the early morning,
     Listen to the lark
     Singing in the daylight,
     Singing out the dark.
     In the early springtime
     Hear the thrushes sing,
     Singing out the winter,
     Singing in the spring.

2   Where the dead leaves rustle
     Under winter trees,
     Everywhere are rising
     Wood anemones;
     Where the snow was lying
     Dead and white and chill,
     Celandines and daisies
     Cover all the hill.

3   Jesus loved the lilies,
     Jesus loved the birds –
     They'd be singing with us
     If they knew the words!
     O, let us say clearly
     What they try to say,
     Birds and buds and children
     Thanking him today.

50

Hurray for Jesus,
Riding to Jerusalem,
Riding to the city
Up a steep and dusty track.
Hurray for Jesus,
Riding to Jerusalem,
Riding there in triumph
On a little donkey's back.

1   Wave palms in the air,
     Spread your bright cloaks everywhere
     And sing, sing, sing.
     Shout out: This is great.
     Jesus enters through the gate –
     Our King.

2   Children wild with joy –
     Every girl and every boy;
     They wave, wave, wave.
     Only we know why
     Christ our King has come to die,
     And save.

51

1   We have a king who rides a donkey,
We have a king who rides a donkey,
We have a king who rides a donkey
And his name is Jesus.

        Jesus, the king, is risen,
Jesus, the king, is risen,
Jesus, the king, is risen
Early in the morning.

2   Trees are waving a royal welcome (3 times)
For the king called Jesus.

3   We have a king who cares for people (3 times)
And his name is Jesus.

4   What shall we do with our life this morning? (3 times)
Give it up in service!

52

1   Who can see the great wind blow?
Neither I nor you.
But it blows the clouds along,
Blows the grass and branches strong.
I can feel the great wind blow,
So can all of you.

2   Who can see God's spirit come?
Neither I nor you.
But he helps us to be strong,
Loving good and fighting wrong.
I can feel God's spirit come,
So can all of you.

53

1   The flowers that grow in the garden
        Dance in the sun,
        Dance in the sun,
    The flowers that grow in the garden
        Thank the Lord for the sun.

2   The birds that fly in the tree tops

3   The cows and sheep in the meadows

4   The fish that swim in the river

5   Then let all children gaily singing

54

1   Look for signs that summer's done,
Winter's drawing near.
Watch the changing colours come,
Turning of the year.
See the flowers' final blaze
In the morning's misty haze,
Sing a thankful song of praise,
Autumn time is here.

2   See the fields are bare and brown,
Feel the nights turn cold.
Lamps are early lit in town,
Hunter's moon shines gold.
Thank you, God, for rest and food,
For the Harvest safely stored,
Sing a song to praise the Lord
As the year grows old.

55

1   When the corn is planted
In the deep dark bed,
Mothers know their children
Will have daily bread.

2   God sends sun and showers,
Birds sing overhead,
While the corn is growing
For our daily bread.

3   When the corn is gathered,
Stored in barn and shed,
Then we all are thankful
For our daily bread.

56

1   The farmer comes to scatter the seed,
Scatter the seed, scatter the seed,
The farmer comes to scatter the seed
Over the fields so brown.

2   God sends the sun, God sends the rain,
Over again, over again,
God sends the sun, God sends the rain,
Over the fields so brown.

3   Up come the green shoots peeping through,
First one by one, then two by two,
Up come the green shoots peeping through,
Under the sky so blue.

4   The waving corn all golden brown,
Golden brown, golden brown,
The farmer comes to cut it down,
Under the sky so blue.

5   Then praise our God who makes it grow,
Makes it grow, makes it grow,
To feed his people here below,
Blessing and love to show.

57

1   See how the snowflakes are falling,
Falling so gentle and white,
Coming from God in their beauty,
All through the day and the night.

2   White are the hills and the meadows,
White are the roofs of the town,
Softly, so softly are falling
Feathery snowflakes down.

58

1   At half past three we go home to tea,
Or maybe at quarter to four;
And ten pairs of feet go running up the street
And in at their own front door:
And it's rough and tumble, rattle and noise,
Mothers and fathers, girls and boys;
Baby in the carry-cot, cat by the stove;
A little bit of quarrelling,
A lot of love.

2   Lord Jesus taught that his children ought
To forgive one another each day,
And to give and take for his dear sake;
So help us, Lord, we pray:
For it's rough and tumble, rattle and noise,
Mothers and fathers, girls and boys;
Baby in the carry-cot, cat by the stove;
A little bit of quarrelling,
But much more love.

59

We're going home, sh, sh,
We're going home, sh, sh,
We're going home to Dad and Mum, sh, sh.
It's time to go, sh, sh,
It's time to go, sh, sh,
Because the day is nearly done, sh, sh.
And now we ask you, God,
Keep us this night
Quite safe from harm
'Till morning light.
We're going home, sh, sh,
We're going home, sh, sh,
And so good night to everyone.

Index of first lines